READ & COLOUR
BIBLE STORIES
FROM THE OLD TESTAMENT

35 STORIES TO READ AND COLOUR

In the Beginning

A long time ago God saw a big, dark, empty space. He wondered how he could fill it.

God decided to make some light. He made the bright sun for the day and the soft moon for the night.

Out of the big, blue sea he made dry land appear and beautiful trees and sweet smelling plants to grow upon it.

But it was quiet, so God made the creatures of the world: fish to swim, birds to fly, and animals to walk.

God looked at what he had made and said it was very good.

(Genesis 1)

God made the world and all that's in it.

Adam and Eve

When God finished his creation he decided to make men and women. First he made a man and called him Adam, and then he made a woman and called her Eve. The two lived in a beautiful garden.

God told them that they could eat any of the delicious fruit in the garden, except from one tree: the tree of knowledge. But one day a naughty snake came, and tempted Eve to eat an apple from the tree.

God was angry with her, and he sent Adam and Eve away from the garden, leaving an angel to guard the gate.

(Genesis 3:6)

Adam and Eve eat the forbidden fruit.

Noah Builds an Ark

The people of the earth were bad and did not listen to God.

God chose a man called Noah to build a large boat called an ark and to fill it with two of every animal on earth.

The rain came down, and the floods came up, but everyone in the ark was safe. The rain fell, but when it stopped, a rainbow appeared in the sky.

Noah now sent a dove to find out if there was any dry land. It came back with a tree branch, and Noah knew that God had kept his promise and saved them.

(Genesis 6:13–22)

Noah and the great ark.

The Tower of Babel

One day some naughty people decided to build a very tall tower, so tall that it would reach heaven itself, far up into the sky. At that time everyone spoke the same language and could understand each other. But God was angry with the people who tried to build the tower and make themselves as important as him. God wanted to punish the people, so he made it so that they all spoke in different languages and could not understand each other. They could not work together on the tower. The tower was never finished, and the people went away.

(Genesis 11:1–9)

The unfinished tower of Babel.

God's Promise to Abraham

In a city called Ur lived a man named Abraham. He had lots of money and was very important. One day God told Abraham to leave Ur and go to a far-off country. God told Abraham that he would bless him. He told Abraham how much he loved him. So God thought of a way to show his love. He showed him first the night sky. "Do you see all the stars? You will have more descendants than there are stars in the sky. All you need to do is trust me." Abraham was amazed, and he placed his trust in God all his days.

(Genesis 11:31 – 12:9)

Abraham and Sarah put their trust in God.

Abraham and Sarah's Baby, Isaac

Abraham's wife, Sarah, was an old woman. She didn't think she could ever have a baby. She prayed to God and asked him to send her a son, but she knew it probably wouldn't happen. One day three strangers came to her house. Abraham welcomed the strangers and asked Sarah to prepare them a meal. During the meal the three strangers told Abraham and Sarah that they had a message for them: Sarah would have a baby. When she heard this, Sarah laughed, but God had heard her prayer and gave her a baby boy. They named him Isaac, which means 'laughter'.

(Genesis 15 – 17)

God gives Abraham and Sarah baby Isaac.

Isaac's Bride

Isaac was a busy man. But he was lonely. "I would dearly like a wife," he prayed to God. One day his servant and camels were travelling far away. They stopped at a well but had no bucket to draw water. There was a beautiful young woman at the well. Her name was Rebekah. She slipped her bucket into the cool water and pulled up water for the servant and the camels. The servant thought she would be the perfect wife for Isaac. He asked her family's permission and took Rebekah back with him to marry Isaac.

(Genesis 24)

Isaac finds a wife – Rebekah.

Jacob and Esau

Isaac had twin sons, Esau and Jacob. He wanted to give his blessing to the elder twin, Esau. But Jacob was jealous. He decided to play a trick on his father. Isaac couldn't see very well, so Jacob decided to pretend to be his brother. He put goatskin on his arms, because Esau was a very hairy man. He then took Isaac his food. Isaac reached out and touched Jacob's arm. "This is Esau," thought Isaac and he gave his blessing. Esau was very angry. Jacob was frightened of what Esau might do and ran far away.

(Genesis 25; 27)

Jacob tricks his father, Isaac.

Jacob's Dream

Jacob was far from home. He was very tired after a long day of walking. He lay down on the hard ground and put a rock under his head as a pillow. He looked up at the stars and was soon asleep. As he slept, Jacob saw the heavens open and a great, gold ladder leading to heaven. Up and down the ladders moved bright angels. When Jacob awoke he knew it was a special place. He made a pile of rocks as a reminder of God's love.

(Genesis 28:10–22)

Jacob finds a special place and feels God's love.

Joseph and His Brothers

Jacob had twelve sons, but his favourite son was Joseph. He gave Joseph a wonderful, multi-coloured coat. His brothers were jealous. They sold him as a slave, dipped his coat in goat's blood and told Jacob he had been killed by a wild animal. Joseph worked hard as a slave in Egypt and became the King's favourite. Meanwhile, there was a famine and Jacob and his family had no food. They came to Egypt to buy food. Joseph was very happy to see his brothers again. Jacob and the brothers lived happily in Egypt with Joseph.

(Genesis 37)

Joseph is very happy to see his brothers again.

Baby Moses is Saved

Many years later in Egypt, God's people had been made slaves. The cruel King was afraid that God's people, the Jews, would become powerful. He ordered that all Jewish newborn baby boys should be killed. One mother put her baby boy in a basket and hid it in the reeds by the riverbank. She asked her daughter, Miriam, to watch it. The Egyptian Princess came to the riverbank and found the baby boy. "I will keep this beautiful baby," she said. "I will call him Moses." Miriam told the princess that she knew the perfect woman to look after the baby for her and ran to fetch her mother.

(Exodus 1:1,2,10)

"I will keep this beautiful baby," said the Egyptian Princess. "I will call him Moses."

Moses and the Red Sea

The Jews were being ill-treated in Egypt. Moses asked the King, the Pharaoh, to let the Jews leave, but he refused. God sent many troubles to the Egyptian people until the Pharaoh allowed Moses to take the Jews out of Egypt. Moses set out with his people, but the Pharaoh changed his mind and sent his soldiers to bring them back. The Red Sea was in front of them. How were they to escape? Moses prayed to God. God told Moses what to do. Moses stretched out his hand and a strong wind parted the sea. Moses led the Jews through to safety. The sea closed behind them and the soldiers were stuck in the mud.

(Exodus 13 – 15)

Moses leads his people to safety.

God's Ten Rules

God wanted to help people. They were being wicked and needed some new rules. He asked Moses to meet him. So Moses climbed up the high mountain. When he got to the top, God gave Moses two stone tablets. He told him to write on them. God gave Moses ten rules for the people to live good lives by. Moses carved God's words into the stone so the people could see. "If they love me, they will follow all of these rules," God said. Moses took the tablets and showed them to his people. These are called the Ten Commandments.

(Exodus 19 – 20)

God gives Moses the Ten Commandments.

Joshua and the Walls of Jericho

God told the Israelites that they were to conquer Jericho. They would win the battle with his help. Each day seven priests were to walk around the walls of the city with the people for seven days. On the seventh day they walked around the high walls seven times and on the seventh time they blew their trumpets and shouted. When they did this, the noise was so great that the walls of Jericho came tumbling down and the Israelites were able to enter. Thanks to God they had won a great victory!

(Joshua 5 – 6)

God gives Joshua victory at Jericho.

Deborah Fights a Battle

Deborah was a prophetess. God spoke to her and gave her messages for his people. One day he told her to tell his servant Barak to fight a battle against a wicked man called Sisera. Barak wasn't sure what to do, but Deborah told him that God has said he would be victorious. So at the foot of the Mountain called Tabor, Barak went into battle as directed by Deborah. He won a great victory and he thanked God for it. Deborah knew that it was God's doing, and she rejoiced that God had again rescued the Israelites from evil people.

(Judges 4 – 5)

Deborah directs Barak for the battle.

Gideon and the Midianites

God's people lived in the land of Canaan. For seven years the Midianite armies attacked and robbed them. God sent an angel to tell Gideon, a farmer, that he would rescue his people from the Midianites. God told Gideon to take just 300 soldiers and, instead of swords and spears, to take trumpets and jars. Gideon was afraid but believed God's word. They went to the Midianite camp at night and blew their trumpets and broke the jars, making a huge noise. The Midianites ran away in terror. God gave his people victory!

(Judges 6 – 7)

Gideon and his men blew their trumpets and broke the jars, making a huge noise.

Strong Samson

One day a boy was born. God's angel told his mother, "Your son, Samson, will save everyone from your enemies, the Philistines. He must never cut his hair or drink wine." Samson grew into a mighty warrior. One day Samson was attacked by a fierce lion. Samson was not afraid and fought it with just his own two hands – he was that strong. Samson fought with the Philistines, who were enemies of his people. They tried to capture him, but he was too strong and always escaped. God had given him his amazing strength!

(Judges 13; 16)

God gives Samson amazing strength.

Samson is Captured

The Philistines needed to find out what made Samson strong. They asked his friend Delilah to find out and offered her money. Samson told her how God had given him great strength if he did not cut his hair. When he was asleep, Delilah asked a man to shave his long hair off. The Philistines captured Samson and chained him to the temple pillars. But Samson's hair began to grow, and so did his strength. Samson broke free and pulled the temple down. After this, God's people were free from their enemies.

(Judges 13; 16)

Samson brings the temple down.

Ruth and Naomi

Naomi was a widow. She cared for her family. Ruth was married to Naomi's son and greatly loved Naomi. Ruth's husband had died as well. Naomi was tired and she wanted to return to her own home. It was a long way away. Ruth would not let Naomi go on her own, so she travelled back with her. It was hard for Ruth, and she often felt lonely, but she knew she was doing the right thing in taking care of Naomi. God saw that she was faithful. He sent Boaz to marry Ruth and support her and Naomi.

(Book of Ruth)

Ruth does not leave Naomi's side.

Samuel is Born

Hannah really wanted to have a child. She thought she was too old to have one. She prayed hard to God. She went to the priest Eli and asked for his blessing. Eli blessed her with wine. Hannah found out she would have a baby. She gave birth to a son, and she named him Samuel. Hannah knew that he was special and was a gift from God. She returned to the Temple to give praise to God and offer her son in his service. The priest Eli was there to accept Samuel. Samuel would become a great prophet.

(1 Samuel 1 – 2)

Eli, the priest, blesses young Samuel.

God Calls to Samuel

Samuel was fast asleep in the Temple when he heard a voice calling out, "Samuel!" He thought it must be his teacher, Eli. He went to Eli and asked him what he wanted. Eli said he hadn't called. Samuel must be hearing things. Samuel fell back to sleep and the same thing happened. Still Eli said it wasn't him. Samuel settled down again, and again a voice called. This time Eli knew it was the Lord. He told Samuel to return and say, "I am here Lord, your servant is listening." By listening to God's special message, Samuel became a servant of God.

(1 Samuel 3:1–19)

"I am here Lord, your servant is listening," said Samuel.

David, the Young Shepherd

David was a young shepherd. He was the youngest in his family. He always got the hardest jobs, such as being out with the sheep. He was tired one day and sat watching the sheep. David played a tune on his harp to the sheep. Just then a stranger appeared and came towards him. The man was Samuel. He took a bottle of oil out of his bag and poured the thick oil on David's head. David was shocked. The man said that David was called by God to be the King of Israel. David was surprised, but he listened to God's call.

(1 Samuel 16)

David, the shepherd, gets a special message.

David Fights Goliath

David was just a young boy but he offered to face the strongest soldier of the Philistine army. This was the terrifying giant Goliath. David only had one small weapon, a sling. He collected five small pebbles and walked across the valley towards the Philistine army. Goliath roared with laughter when he saw David. But David wasn't afraid; he trusted in God. He took one of the pebbles and with his sling he threw it at the giant. It hit Goliath in the middle of his head sending him to the ground with a thud. Young David had beaten the giant soldier.

(1 Samuel 17)

Young David defeats the giant Goliath.

David's Songs to God

King David had loved music since he was a young boy. It was a gift from God. He had written songs when he had been keeping the sheep in the hills. David loved to praise God, his creator. He decided that he would write more songs in praise of God. He called these songs psalms. He wrote over seventy psalms. He loved to sing them whilst he played his harp. They helped him to think about God and helped other people to sing praises to God. God loved to hear King David sing and praise him.

(Book of Psalms)

King David praises God with music.

Wise King Solomon

Solomon was given great wisdom by God. One day two women came to him. They had a baby with them. Each woman said the baby was hers. Solomon wanted to know who was lying. He asked a soldier to come and cut the baby in half so each woman could have half. One woman told the king to go right ahead. The other woman screamed, begging the king to spare the baby. Solomon realised that it was this woman who was the baby's mother as she did not want the baby to die. Solomon's fame spread throughout the world.

(1 Kings 3:3–15)

King Solomon passes judgement.

Solomon Builds a Temple for God

Solomon knew that he had to build a temple for God. As it was for the worship of God, he wanted the best. He set out and found the greatest craftsmen in the world and brought them to Jerusalem. He also brought the finest stone, finest jewels and finest wood. God had told him what the Temple should look like. It would be huge so that all the people could come and worship God. It would be a way for Solomon to show he loved God. When the Temple was completed, all the people rejoiced and praised God.

(1 Kings 4 – 7)

King Solomon builds a temple for God.

Elijah and the Ravens

Elijah was very hungry. He was out in the hot, wild desert and he had nothing to eat. He had managed to find a stream and had sat down. He was very tired. He had gone to pray to God and had taken nothing with him. God knew that Elijah was a good man who wanted to work for him. So God thought of a way to feed Elijah. He called upon the ravens who spread their black wings and went in search of food. The ravens soon found bread and flew back to Elijah carrying it in their beaks.

(1 Kings 16 – 17)

The ravens feed Elijah in the desert.

Elijah and the Widow

Elijah was travelling through the countryside. He didn't have any food and was hungry and tired. He met an old widow on the road, and he asked her if she could spare some food. The widow had only a little oil and flour, enough for one last meal for herself and her son. Elijah promised her God would help. He told the widow to mix the oil and flour together to make bread. The widow was not sure if she should believe Elijah. But as she began to cook, she couldn't believe it. There was bread for her, for Elijah and for days to come!

(1 Kings 17:7–16)

There was bread for the widow, for Elijah and for days to come!

Elisha Heals Naaman

Naaman was a powerful general. He was also sick and had an illness on his skin. He wanted help. He asked God's prophet Elisha what he should do. Elisha told Naaman that he should wash seven times in the river Jordan and then his skin would be as good as new. Naaman was angry as he didn't want to go into the dirty river Jordan. Elisha told him that he must. Eventually Naaman agreed, and he went into the river seven times. On the seventh time when Naaman came out of the water, his skin was healed.

(2 Kings 5:1–15)

Naaman is cured by the Prophet Elisha.

Little King Joash

Joash was only seven years old when his uncle, the priest Jehoiada, crowned him King. King Joash was a wise and good young man who loved God. He wanted to worship God always and paid to have the Temple restored. It was because he loved God so much that God chose him to rule over the people. Many people didn't think that someone as young as Joash could make a difference. Joash worked very hard at serving God well. Each one of us is called by God to serve him no matter how young we are. Will you serve God like young King Joash?

(2 Kings 11 – 12)

Little Joash is crowned King.

God Protects Three Men in a Furnace

Three Israelites, Shadrach, Meshach and Abednego, were to be placed in the burning, fiery furnace as a punishment for praying to God. They were not scared; they trusted in God. They were placed in the hot furnace. Only then, the people watching saw there weren't just three people in the furnace but four. The men had been joined by an Angel of God who was helping keep them safe. No matter how hot the furnace got, the men were not harmed. The people were amazed. The three men knew that God had helped them as they trusted in him.

(Daniel 3)

Shadrach, Meshach and Abednego are saved from burning by an Angel of God.

Daniel and the Lions

Daniel was to be killed. Evil men had plotted against him and tricked the king into putting him into the lions' den. The lions were big and hungry. Daniel would not survive the night, they thought. Once Daniel was in the den, a rock was pulled across the entrance. Daniel knelt and prayed. The lions did not wake up. They did not move. Daniel prayed all night and the lions did not hurt him. The next morning the king came expecting Daniel to have been eaten. Daniel was alive. The king knew Daniel's God had saved him.

(Daniel 6)

The king knew Daniel's God had saved him.

Nehemiah Rebuilds Jerusalem

After a long time away from Jerusalem, Nehemiah returned to find the city in ruins. All the buildings were gone, there were just rocks everywhere and there was nowhere to worship God. Nehemiah decided that the people needed to be encouraged, so he gathered them together and told them stories of God's love. This made the people happy. Nehemiah told them they needed to rebuild the holy city. The people began to rebuild, and soon the city was as glorious as before.

(Nehemiah 1 – 2)

Nehemiah gets the people to rebuild Jerusalem.

Queen Esther Saves the Jews

Esther knew evil people were trying to trick her husband, King Xerxes of Persia, into hurting her people, the Jews. Esther planned a big banquet of all the king's favourite foods. She invited the king and, as he ate and drank, she spoke to him about her people. She wasn't sure if the king would be angry with her for what she said, but she trusted in God and was brave. She continued to speak to him and beg him to change the law. Xerxes was impressed with Esther's love for her people and so he saved the Jews.

(Book of Esther)

Queen Esther begs King Xerxes to keep the Jews safe.

Jonah and the Huge Fish

God asked Jonah to tell the people of Nineveh to stop being bad. But Jonah did not want to do this and ran away from God. He was on a boat and there was a terrible storm. The sailors were scared. Jonah is to blame, they thought. So they picked him up and threw him into the deep, dark sea. As Jonah sank down, a big fish swallowed him. Jonah prayed in the belly of the huge fish. God told the fish to swim to shore. It spat Jonah out. Jonah knew God had saved him, and he went to Nineveh with God's message.

(Jonah 1 – 3)

God told the fish to swim to shore and spit Jonah out.